Orchestrations for Orff Instruments

SERIES AUTHORS

Judy Bond
Coordinating Author

René Boyer-White

Margaret Campbelle-duGard

Marilyn Copeland Davidson
Coordinating Author

Robert de Frece

Mary Goetze
Coordinating Author

Doug Goodkin

Betsy M. Henderson

Michael Jothen

Carol King

Vincent P. Lawrence
Coordinating Author

Nancy L. T. Miller

Ivy Rawlins

Susan Snyder
Coordinating Author

Macmillan/McGraw-Hill School Publishing Company
New York • Columbus

Acknowledgments

Grateful acknowledgment is given to the following authors, composers, and publishers. Every effort has been made to trace the ownership of all copyrighted material and to secure the necessary permissions to reprint these selections. In the case of some selections for which acknowledgment is not given, extensive research has failed to locate the copyright holders.

CPP/Belwin, Inc. for *Shabat Shalom* by Sholom Secunda, Arranged by Judy Bond. Copyright © 1976 BELWIN MILLS. Used by permission of CPP/Belwin, Inc., Miami, FL. All rights reserved.

Geordie Music Publishing Company for *Peace Round*, © 1964, 1971 Jean Ritchie, Geordie Music Publishing Company.

Memphis Musicraft Publications for *Goin' to Boston* from HEARING AMERICA, AMERICAN FOLK SONGS FOR UNCHANGED VOICES AND ORFF INSTURMENTS, © 1981 Memphis Musicraft Publications, 3149 Southern Ave., Memphis, TN 38111.

Konnie Saliba for *Simple Gifts*, arranged by Konnie Saliba.

Jim Solomon for *Mango Walk*, a Jamaican calypso arranged by Jim Solomon.

Sweet Pipes Inc. for *Gao Shan Ching (A-Li Mountain's Dancing Song)* from MELODIES FROM THE FAR EAST by Marilyn Copeland Davidson. Copyright © 1990 Sweet Pipes Inc. Used by permission.

Contributing Writer
Anna Marie Spallina

Macmillan/McGraw-Hill School Division
10 Union Square East
New York, New York 10003

Printed in the United States of America

ISBN 0-02-295083-4 / 5

1 2 3 4 5 6 7 8 9 BAW 99 98 97 96 95 94

Table of Contents

		PUPIL'S EDITION page	ORFF MASTER page
UNIT 1			
0•1	We Will Raise a Ruckus Tonight	10	2
0•2	Ev'rybody Loves Saturday Night	19	5
0•3	Peace Round	43	8
UNIT 2			
0•4	Mango Walk	56	10
0•5	Gau Shan Ching *(Ali Mountain)*	60	14
0•6	Zum gali gali	80	19
UNIT 3			
0•7	Shabat Shalom	107	22
UNIT 4			
0•8	Erie Canal	154	25
0•9	Down the River	156	30
0•10	Et tan' patate là cuite *(Potato's Done)*	164	35
0•11	Pat Works on the Railway	169	39
Encore			
0•12	Simple Gifts	191	44
UNIT 5			
0•13	Ezekiel Saw de Wheel	214	51
0•14	El quelite *(The Village)*	238	55

		PUPIL'S EDITION page	ORFF MASTER page
UNIT 6			
0•15	Joe Turner Blues	261	65
Celebrations			
0•16	Nottamun Town	293	68
0•17	The Horseman	295	71
Music Library			
0•18	Nine Hundred Miles	345	74
0•19	Going to Boston	365	77

INTRODUCTION

The Orff approach to music education actively involves students in speech, movement, singing, instrument playing, and drama. Developed by German composer Carl Orff (1895–1982), the approach is based on the instinctive learning behavior of children. Improvisation and movement permeate the learning process, and use of the specially designed Orff instruments enables children to create and perform ensemble music at every level.

The materials used include both folk and composed music, along with chants, rhymes, and poetry. As students experience this music they develop a musical vocabulary and skills that may then be used to create original works.

Orff orchestrations have been created for selected songs in SHARE THE MUSIC. Along with each orchestration are teaching suggestions. The teaching suggestions include:

Instrumentation—A chart is given showing letters for specific bars used on mallet instruments for each song. Unused bars are shown as □. All parts except timpani are commonly written in the treble clef. Bass xylophone and bass metallophone sound an octave below the written pitch. Soprano xylophone, soprano metallophone, and alto glockenspiel sound an octave above the written pitch. The soprano glockenspiel sounds two octaves above the written pitch. The alto xylophone and alto metallophone sound at the written pitch.

Teaching the Orchestration—A suggested basic teaching sequence is given for each orchestration. In orchestrations the bass part is usually the most important. Students must be secure with this part before other parts are added. Except for the bass pattern, most parts may be considered optional. The teacher may choose to use only some of the suggested orchestration depending on circumstances—such as ability of students, the time available, or the accessibility of specific instruments. Many of the arrangements can be musically satisfying with only the bass part and one other part added for tone color and/or rhythmic interest.

Form—Suggestions for the final form may include introductions, interludes, codas, chants, and opportunities for improvisation.

Noteworthy—This is a list of important musical elements that can be reinforced with the orchestration.

The Orff approach can infuse music classes with a spirit of cooperation and joy, enabling students to develop concentration and perception skills, increased aesthetic awareness and physical coordination, and a high level of motivation.

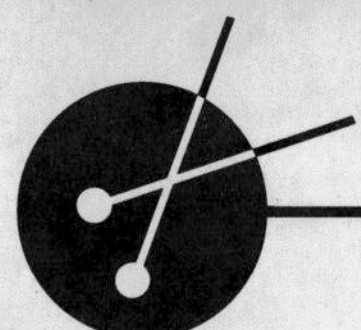

0·1 We Will Raise a Ruckus Tonight

INSTRUMENTATION

AX	**C D** □ □ **G** □ □ □ □ □ □ □ □	guiro, tambourine
BX	□ **D** □ □ **G** □ □ □ **D E** □ □ □	

TEACHING THE ORCHESTRATION

1. Teach the bass xylophone part.

Have the students:

- Mirror you as they pat the rhythm of the BX part using the following pattern: left-right-right-left-right-right, and sing the song.
- Continue patting the rhythm as they sing the pitch names of the BX part.
- Take turns playing the BX part on any available barred instruments.
- Sing the song as one student plays the BX part.

2. Add the alto xylophone part.

Have the students:

- Pat the rhythm of the AX part with alternating hands on right thigh (G) and left thigh (C and D) as they sing the song.
- Continue patting the rhythm as they sing the pitch names of the AX part.
- Take turns playing the AX part on any available barred instruments.
- Sing the song as some students play the BX and AX parts.

3. Teach the tambourine part.

Have the students:

- Clap eighth notes as they sing the song.
- Take turns playing eighth notes on the tambourine, holding by the rim with one hand and tapping on the tambourine head near the rim with the other hand.

4. Add the güiro part.

Have the students:

- Snap the rhythm of the guiro part as they sing the song.
- Take turns playing the guiro part. Combine with the other parts previously learned. Sing and perform the entire orchestration.

FORM

Verse: Voice, AX, BX, Guiro, Tamb.

NOTEWORTHY

Rhythm:	eighth notes, syncopated pattern (eighth-quarter-eighth)
Melody:	G Major
Harmony:	I-IV-V

0·1 We Will Raise a Ruckus Tonight

African American Jubilee
Adapted by René Boyer-White
Arranged by René Boyer-White

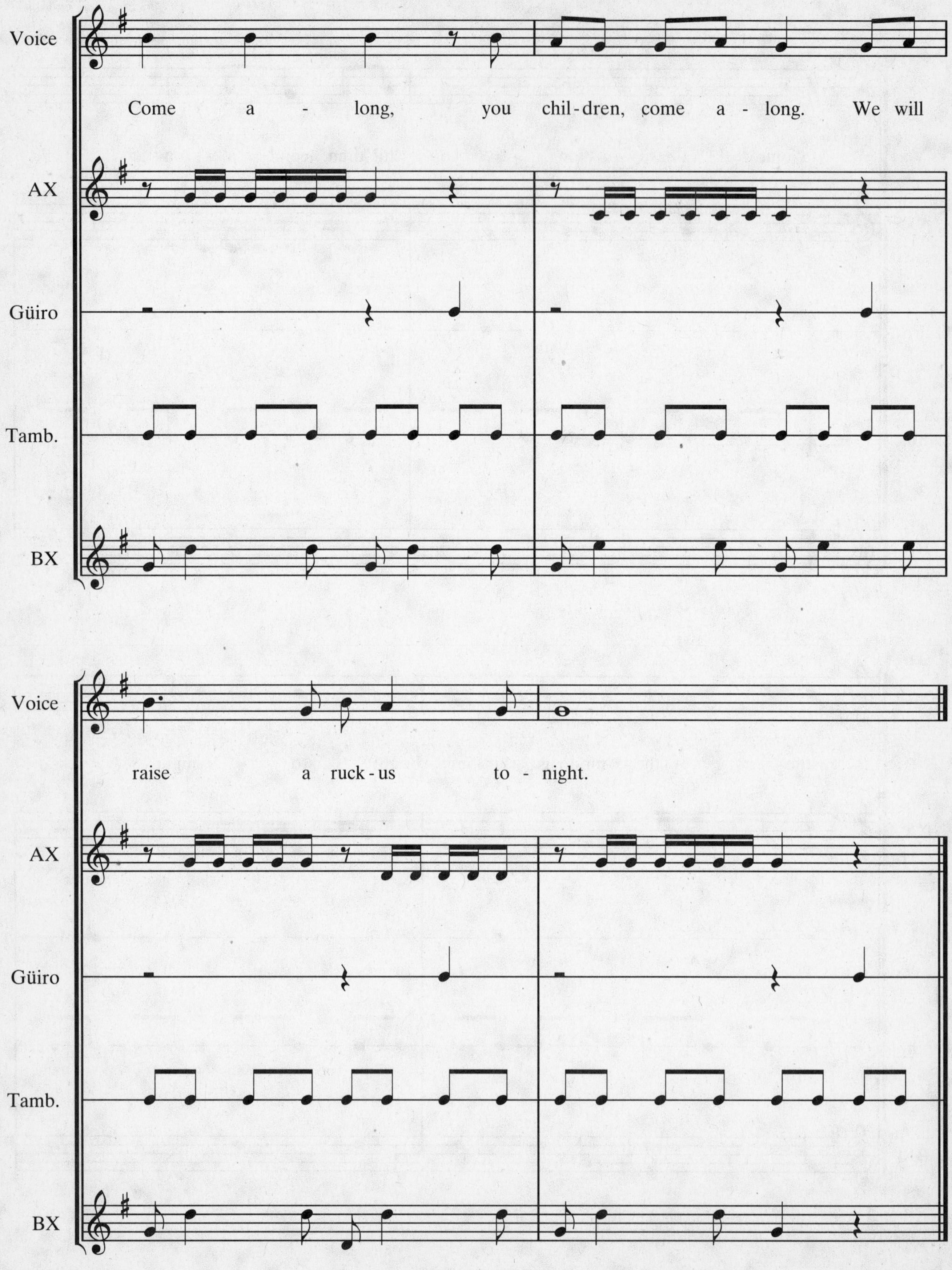

We Will Raise a Ruckus Tonight (continued)

Voice

Come a - long, you chil-dren, come a - long. We will

AX

Güiro

Tamb.

BX

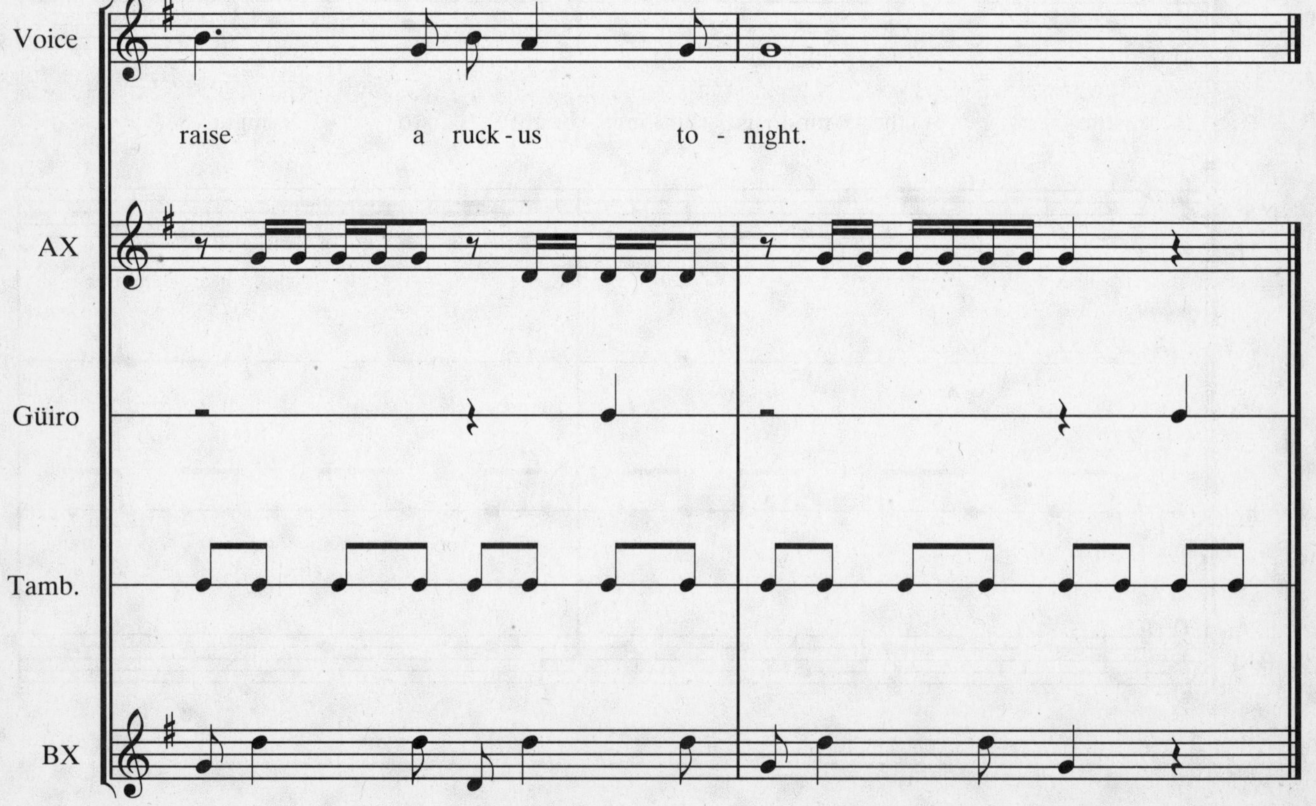

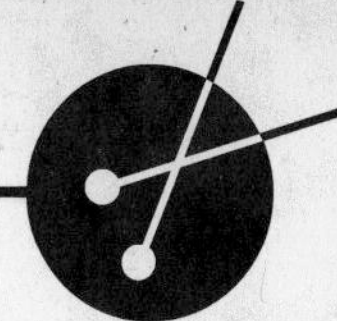

0·2 Ev'rybody Loves Saturday Night

INSTRUMENTATION

AM	□ □ □ F G A B♭ C □ □ □ □ □ □ □	conga 1, conga 2, agogo bell
BX/BM	C □ □ F G □ □ C □ □ □ □ □ □ □	

TEACHING THE ORCHESTRATION

1. **Teach the bass xylophone/bass metallophone part.**

   Have the students:
   - Pat the rhythm of the BX/BM part with alternating hands as they sing the song.
   - Mirror you, showing the pitch relationships by placement of the hand as they pat, and listening as you sing the pitch letter names. (Each student's right hand is always centered on the right thigh, in preparation for playing high C. The left hand shows the F when patting in the center of the left thigh, the G to the right, and the low C to the left.)
   - Sing the pitch letter names while continuing to mirror you, gradually moving the hands away from the thighs to the correct position for playing in the air.
   - Form two groups, one to sing the song while the other sings pitch letter names and plays the part in the air. Switch parts.
   - Transfer this part to any available barred instruments and take turns playing while singing the song.
   - Sing the song as students play the BX/BM part.

2. **Teach the alto metallophone part.**

   Have the students:
   - Mirror you, playing the AM part in the air as they sing the song. (Move both hands in parallel motion, snapping the rhythm to keep the lively feeling of the song.)
   - Follow notation of this part on a chart or chalkboard and sing pitch letter names as you point. (Point to notes in the bottom line first, then the top line. Then have the class sing in two parts on "lai" or another neutral syllable.)
   - Transfer the AM part to any available barred instruments and take turns playing it while some students play the BX part and others sing the song.
   - Sing the song as one student plays the AM part and another plays the BX part.

3. **Teach the percussion parts.**

   Have the students:
   - Learn the percussion parts by playing an imitation game. (Tell the students to copy what you do, and to continue doing the motion, even when you change to a different motion, until you say the magic word *Saturday.* When the magic word is heard, the students change to the new motion, which is then continued until the magic word is heard again. Begin with the conga 1 part, snapping the rhythm. When this is well established, change to patting the conga 2 part. After the two parts have been performed together, call the magic word and the students change to conga 2. The game continues in this manner, with clapping of the agogo bell part.)
   - Form three groups, one to play each percussion part, using the body-percussion sounds above. (Start the conga 1 group. After four measures, add the conga 2 group. After another four measures, add the bell group. Then sing the song.)
   - Transfer the parts to percussion instruments and take turns playing each part separately, and then combining two and three parts. (The conga 1 part should be played on the largest drum available. The conga 2 part should be played with the hand hitting the drum on the eighth notes and a drumstick hitting the edge of the drum on the sixteenth notes. Hold the lower agogo bell so the sound is dead, but allow the higher bell to ring.)
   - Sing the song as students play the percussion parts.

4. **Perform the entire song with accompaniment.**

   Have the students:
   - Review each part and then combine all parts, starting with the BX/BM and AM, then adding percussion all at once or one at a time. (After singing a few verses, you may wish to have an interlude with only the percussion accompaniment while some students improvise.)
   - Plan a final form, using movement, the vocal harmony part, different languages, and improvisation. (See Pupil Edition pp. 20–21 for movement instructions.)

FORM

Verse: Voice, AM, BX, Ag. Bl., Conga 1, Conga 2

NOTEWORTHY

Rhythm:	syncopation, sixteenth rest, sixteenth-note patterns, divided beat, half notes
Melody:	F Major
Harmony:	I-V, two-part vocal harmony

0·2 Ev'rybody Loves Saturday Night

Western African Song
Arranged by Doug Goodkin

Macmillan/McGraw-Hill

Voice
Ev' - ry - bod - y loves Sat - ur-day night.
AM
Ag. Bl.
Conga 1
Conga 2
BX/BM

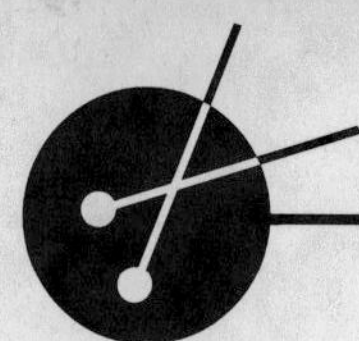

0·3 Peace Round

INSTRUMENTATION

SG/AG	□ □ E □ □ □ □ □ □ □ E □ □ □	triangle/finger cymbals, cabasa, hand drum
AM	□ □ E □ □ □ B □ □ □ □ □ □	
BM	□ □ E □ □ □ B □ □ □ □ □ □	

TEACHING THE ORCHESTRATION

1. **Teach the bass metallophone and alto metallophone part.**

   Have the students:
   - Form two groups. Have the first group pat whole notes on the odd-numbered measures as the second group pats whole notes on the even-numbered measures.
   - Transfer the first group's pats to the BM part and the second group's pats to the AM part. Take turns playing each part on any available barred instruments.
   - Sing the song as some students play the BM and AM parts.

2. **Teach the soprano glockenspiel/alto glockenspiel part.**

   Have the students:
   - Snap the rhythm of the SG/AG part as they sing the song.
   - Take turns playing the SG/AG part on any available barred instruments.
   - Sing the song as some students play the SG/AG, BM and AM parts.

3. **Add the triangle/finger cymbals, cabasa and hand drum parts.**

   Have the students:
   - Divide into three groups and perform the following body percussion:

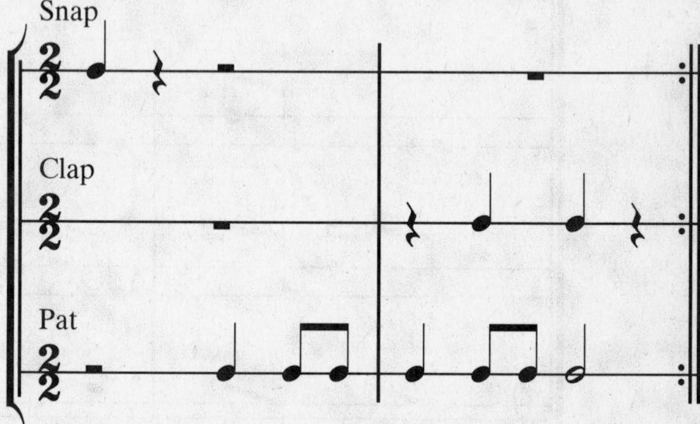

   - Transfer the pats to the hand drum, the claps to the cabasa, and the snaps to the triangle/finger cymbals as in the score.
   - Combine with the barred instrument parts and perform the entire orchestration as they sing the song.

FORM

Canon: Voice, SG/AG, AM/BM, Tri., F. Cym., Cab., HD

NOTEWORTHY

Rhythm: half notes, quarter notes, eighth notes
Melody: E minor
Harmony: bordun

0·3 Peace Round

Old English Canon
Words by Jean Ritchie
Adapted from Psalm 13:1
Arranged by Judy Bond

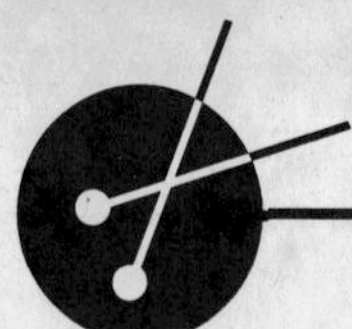

0•4 Mango Walk

INSTRUMENTATION

AG	□ □ □ □ □ **A B♭ C D E F** □ □	maracas, hand drum, conga drum
AX	**C** □ □ □ □ □ □ □ □ □ □ □ □ □ □ □	
BX	**C** □ □ **F** □ □ □ □ □ □ □ □ □ □ □ □	

TEACHING THE ORCHESTRATION

1. Teach the bass xylophone part.

Have the students:

- Mirror you as you pat and clap the rhythm of the BX part (pat on C, clap on F), singing the letter names with you.

2. Teach the conga drum part.

Have the students:

- Say the following words as they pat the rhythm:

- Sing the song as several students take turns playing the pattern on the conga drum. (Other drums may be substituted if conga drums are not available.)

3. Teach the hand drum and alto xylophone parts.

Have the students:

- Say the following words as they pat the rhythm:

- Sing the song a few times as several students take turns playing the hand drum on the word *the* in the chant and playing the alto xylophone on C on the words *mango walk* in the chant.

4. Teach the alto glockenspiel part.

Have the students:

- Sing the alto glockenspiel pitch letter names from a hand staff or from notation on the chalkboard.
- Take turns practicing the part on all the barred instruments.
- Play it on the alto glockenspiel while singing the song.
- Sing the song with all the instrument parts.

5. Teach the maracas, the hand drum, and the conga parts in the interlude.

Have the students:

- Learn the maracas part by echoing with finger snaps and then play it on maracas. Teach the hand drum and conga parts in a similar manner.
- Two at a time, take turns improvising four-measure phrases on the conga drum and hand drums as the maracas accompany them.

6. Teach the dance.

Have the students:

- Form two lines, all facing the front, and learn the following dance.

Note: Except as otherwise noted, arms move forward and backward alternately, imitating the motion of a train, with fingers spread widely apart. (This dance is an alternative to the one for which directions are provided in the Pupil Edition.)

Song:

measures 1-4: Step R Cross L front Step R Cross L behind (Repeat)

measures 5-6: (circling to left) Step L Step R Step L Touch R (and touch L elbow with R hand)

measures 7-8: (circling to right) Step R Step L Step R Touch L (and touch R elbow with L hand)

Interlude:

The couple standing at the rear of the lines improvise a "mango walk" forward between the rows as others do a step-touch in place, alternately touching each elbow with the opposite hand, as above.
(On the alternate repeats of the A section, the dance should be done in the opposite direction.)

- Perform the dance while singing the song, as some students play the instrumental accompaniment.

—Dance by Jim Solomon

FORM

Introduction:	Measures 1-4, AG, AX, BX, HD, Conga
Song:	Voice, *tutti* instruments
Interlude:	Mar., HD
Song:	Voice, *tutti* instruments
Interlude:	Mar., HD
Song:	Voice, *tutti* instruments
Interlude:	Mar., HD
Song:	Voice, *tutti* instruments

NOTEWORTHY

Rhythm:	syncopation
Harmony:	I-V

0·4 Mango Walk

Jamaican Calypso
Arranged by Jim Solomon

Voice
moth - er deed - a tell me that you go man - go walk and
AG
AX
HD
Conga
BX

Fine
Voice
eat all the num - ber 'lev - en.
AG
AX
HD
Conga
BX
Interlude
D.S. al Fine
Voice
(My)
Mar.
HD
Conga

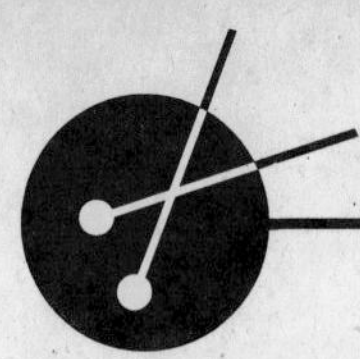

0•5 Gau Shan Ching
(Ali Mountain)

INSTRUMENTATION

BX □□E□□□□□□□E□□□ recorder, finger cymbals, woodblock

TEACHING THE ORCHESTRATION

1. **Teach the bass xylophone part.**

   Have the students:
   - Pat the rhythm of the BX part, using alternating hands, beginning with the left hand. At the same time, they sing the song.
   - Take turns playing the BX part on any available barred instruments.
   - Sing the song as one student plays the BX part.

2. **Add the woodblock and finger cymbals part.**

   Have the students:
   - Clap the rhythm of the woodblock part as they sing the song.
   - Take turns playing the woodblock part with the BX part.
   - Sing the song, snapping on each rest.
   - Have one student play the finger cymbals on each rest in the melody.
   - Sing the song as some students perform the entire orchestration.

3. **Add the recorder part.**

   Have the students:
   - Read the recorder part from the board or other visual.
   - Finger the notes as they sing the pitch names in the correct rhythm of the part.
   - Play the recorder part as some students play the BX part.
   - Gradually combine the recorder parts with the other instrument parts in the song.

FORM

Verse: Voice, BX, F. Cym., WB, Rec.

NOTEWORTHY

Rhythm: eighth notes, sixteenth notes, dotted quarter note
Melody: pentatonic
Harmony: i-octave accompaniment

0·5 Gau Shan Ching
(Ali Mountain)

Taiwanese Folk Song
English Words by Marilyn Davidson
and Judy Bond
Arranged by Marilyn Davidson

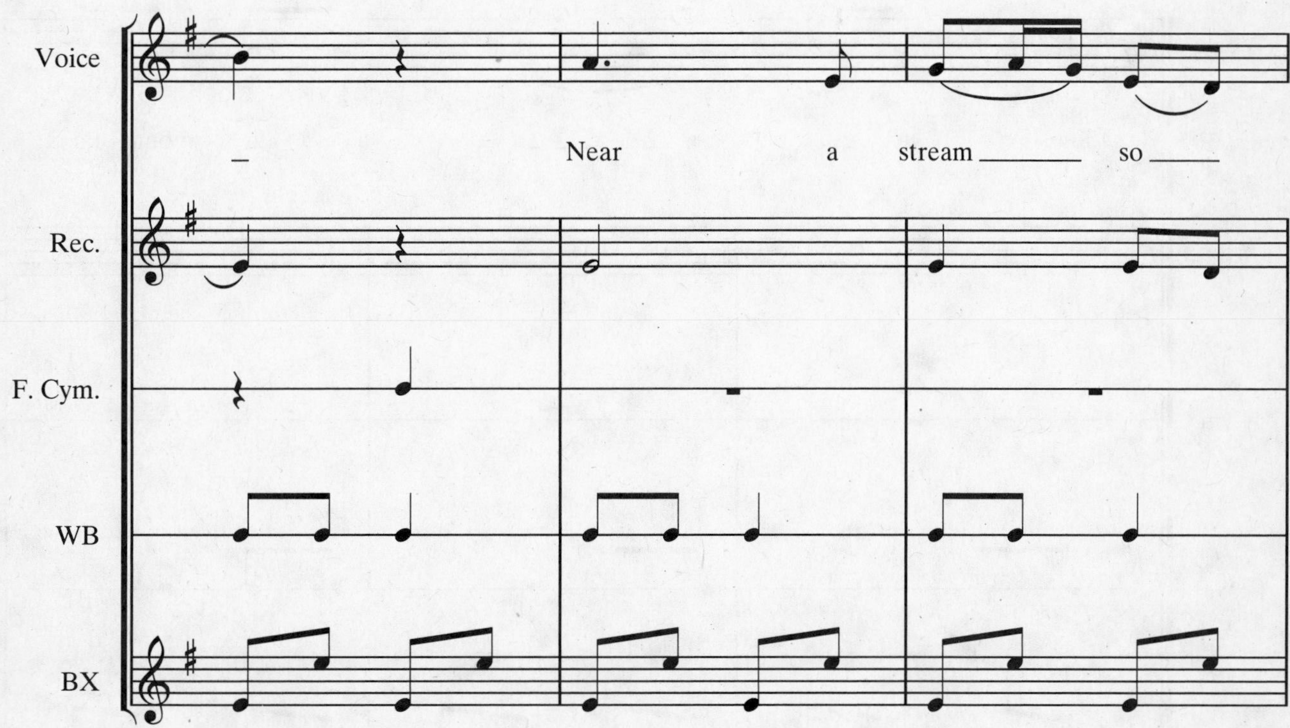

Gau Shan Ching (continued)

Voice
dan - cers, grace - ful and strong.
Rec.
F. Cym.
WB
BX
Voice
Ah!
Rec.
F. Cym.
WB
BX

Gau Shan Ching (continued)

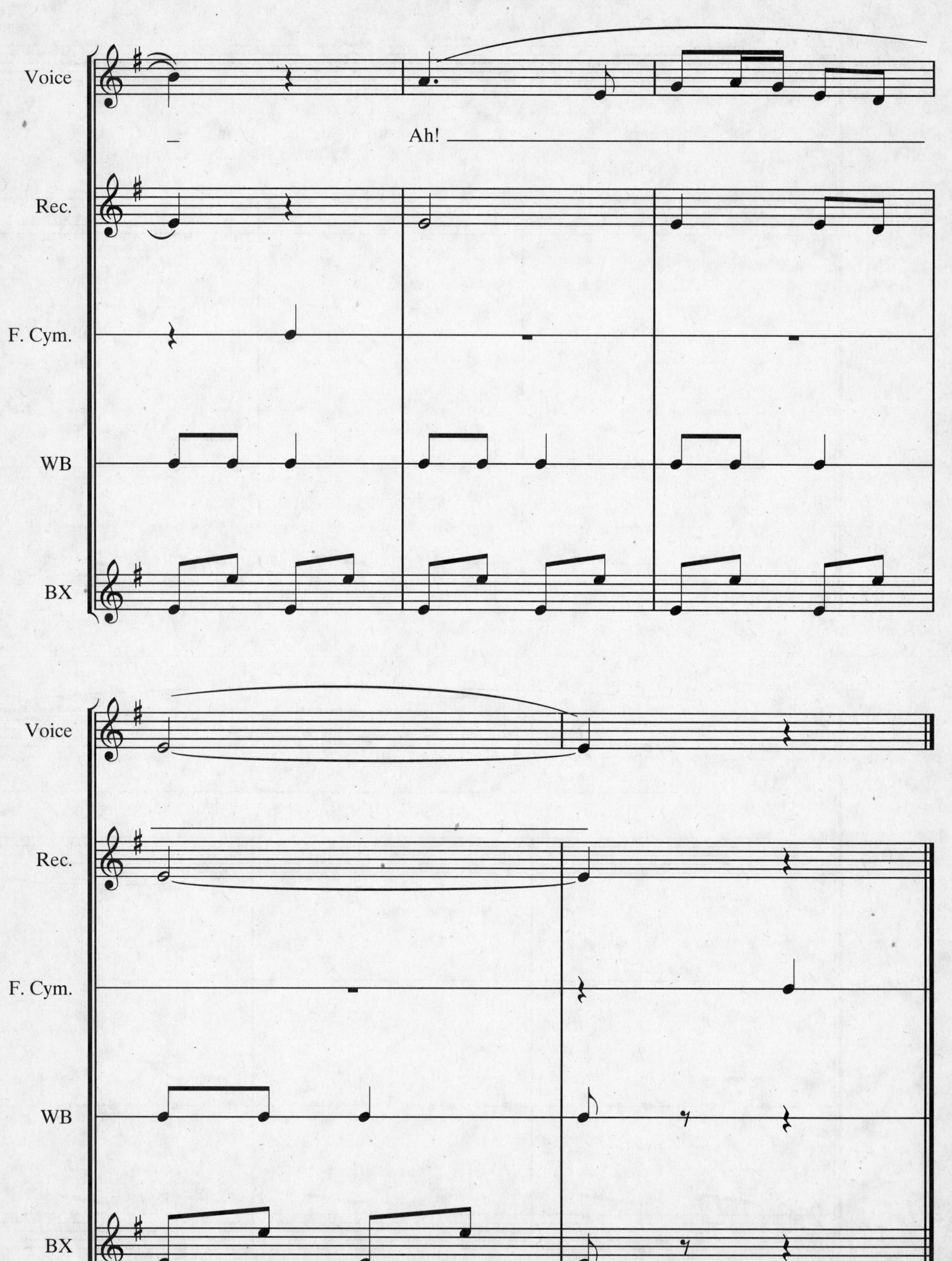

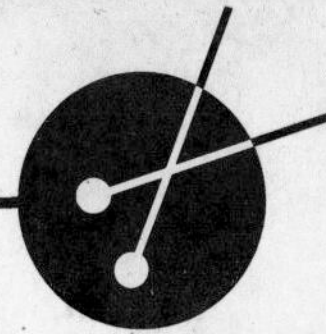

0•6 Zum gali gali

INSTRUMENTATION

AG	□ □ □ □ □ A B □ □ E □ □ □	tambourine, bongo drums
SX/AX	□ □ E □ □ □ □ □ □ □ E □ □ □	
BX	□ □ E □ □ A B C □ □ □ □ □	

TEACHING THE ORCHESTRATION

1. Teach the bass xylophone part.

Have the students:
- Pat the rhythm of the BX part as they sing the song.
- Play the BX part in the air, mirroring you.
- Take turns playing the BX part on any available barred instruments.
- Sing the song as one student plays the BX part.

2. Add the alto glockenspiel part.

Have the students:
- Snap the rhythm of the AG part as they sing the song.

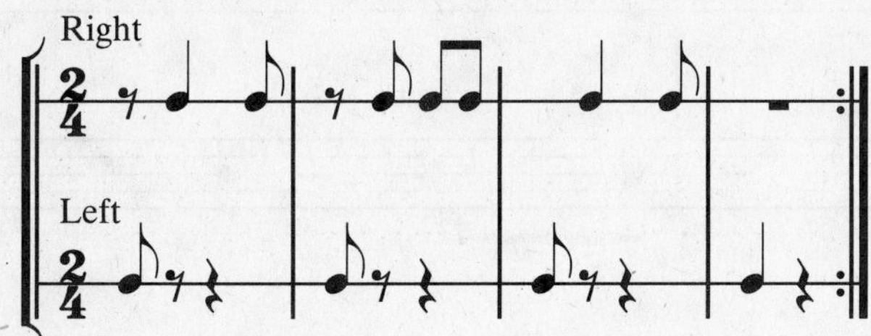

- Take turns playing the AG part on any available barred instruments.
- Sing the song as some students play the AG and BX parts.

3. Teach the soprano xylophone/alto xylophone part.

Have the students:
- Pat the rhythm of the SX/AX part with alternating hands as they sing the song.
- Take turns playing the SX/AX part on any available barred instruments.
- Combine with the other instrument parts previously learned.

4. Teach the bongo drums part.

Have the students:
- Mirror you as they pat the rhythm of the bongo drums part as shown below:

- Take turns playing the bongo part as they sing the song.

5. Add the tambourine part.

Have the students:
- Clap the rhythm of the tambourine part as they sing the song. Decide which part is rhythmically the opposite of this part. (the BX part)
- Take turns playing the tambourine part with the BX part.
- Perform the entire orchestration as they sing the song.

FORM

Round: Voice, AG, SX/AX, BX, Tam., Bongo

NOTEWORTHY

Rhythm: eighth notes, sixteenth notes, syncopation
Harmony: i-iv

0·6 Zum gali gali

Israeli Work Song
Arranged by Judy Bond

Ⓑ Verse
Voice
Pi - o - neers work hard on the land,
As they la - bor all day long,
AG
SX/AX
Tamb.
Bongos
BX
Voice
Men and wom - en work hand in hand.
They lift their voi - ces in song.
AG
SX/AX
Tamb.
Bongos
BX

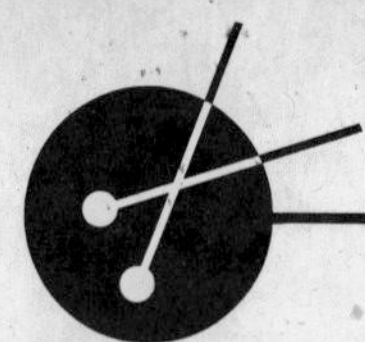

0·7 Shabat Shalom

INSTRUMENTATION

AG	□ □ □ □ **G A B♭** □ **D** □ □ □ □ □ □	tambourine, finger cymbals
SX/AX	□ **D E F G A B♭ C D** □ □ □ □ □ □	
BM	□ **D** □ □ **G A B♭** □ □ □ □ □ □ □ □	
BX	□ **D** □ □ □ □ □ □ □ **D** □ □ □ □ □ □	

TEACHING THE ORCHESTRATION

1. Teach the bass metallophone part.

Have the students:
- Pat the rhythm of the BM part as they sing the first four measures of the song.
- Play the BM part in the air, mirroring you.
- Learn the pitches by playing in the air (mirroring you) while echoing you, or reading the pitches from notation on a chart or the chalkboard. (Students are likely to master this part more quickly if notation is presented visually. If the echo process is used, pitches must be learned for each hand separately.)
- Take turns playing the BM part on any available barred instruments.
- Sing the first four measures as one student plays the BM part.

2. Add the alto glockenspiel part.

Have the students:
- Clap the rhythm of the AG part as they sing the first four measures.
- Learn the pitches by echoing you or reading from notation.
- Clap the rhythm of the AG part as they sing pitch names of the part.
- Take turns playing the AG part on any available barred instruments.
- Sing the first four measures as some students play the AG and BM parts.

3. Teach the bass xylophone part in the last two measures.

Have the students:
- Pat the rhythm of the BX part as they sing the last two measures.
- Learn that the pitches are octave Ds and sing this part while playing it in the air, mirroring you.
- Take turns playing the BX part on any available barred instruments.
- Sing the last two measures as one student plays the BX part.

4. Teach the soprano xylophone/alto xylophone part in the last two measures.

Have the students:
- Pat the rhythm of the SX/AX part with alternating hands as they sing the B section of the song.
- Play the SX/AX part in the air, mirroring you.
- Sing the SX/AX part on a neutral syllable while playing in the air, first echoing you.
- Analyze this part, noting that it is the D natural minor scale with repetition of the low D on the word rhythm of "Shabat Shalom."
- In two groups, sing the melody and the SX/AX part together. (Sing the SX/AX part on a neutral syllable and play it in the air at the same time. Switch groups so all students practice this part.)
- Take turns playing the SX/AX part on any available barred instruments.
- Sing the last two measures as some students play the SX/AX and BX parts.

5. Teach the tambourine and finger cymbals parts.

Have the students:
- Perform the following body percussion:

- Transfer the claps to the tambourine part and the snap to the finger cymbals.
- Perform the entire orchestration as they sing the song.
- Form groups for singing, playing, and movement. (See Teachers Edition pages 107 and 129 instructions.) Decide on the number of repetitions and perform the entire piece with singing, movement, and orchestration.

FORM

Song: Voice, *tutti* instruments

NOTEWORTHY

Rhythm: syncopation, eighth notes
Harmony: i-iv

0•7 Shabat Shalom

Words and Music by N. Frankel
Arranged by Judy Bond

D.C. al Fine
Voice
Sha - bat, sha - bat, sha - bat, sha - bat sha - lom.
AG
SX/AX
F. Cym.
Tamb.
BX
BM

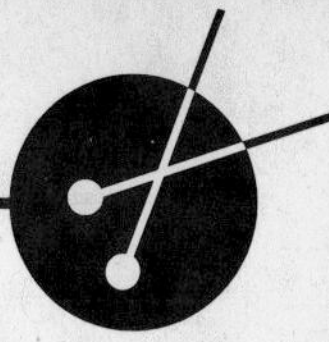

0·8 Erie Canal

INSTRUMENTATION

AG/SX	**C D** □ □ □ **A** □ **C D** □ □ □ **A**
SM	□ □ □ **F** □ □ □ **C** □ □ □ □ □ □
AX/AM	□ **D E F G A** □ **C D** □ **F** □ □
BX/BM	**C D** □ **F G A B♭C** □ □ □ □ □ □

recorders, finger cymbals, woodblock, güiro

TEACHING THE ORCHESTRATION

1. Teach the instrument parts for the verse.

Have the students:

- Form five groups, one for each part: AG/SX, AX/AM, F. Cym., WB, BX/BM.
- Learn the rhythm of each part with body percussion.
- Learn the pitches of each barred instrument part. (These may be taught through echoing while doing the body percussion, or by reading from your hand staff or from notation.)
- Sing the verse, as one person from each group plays the part on an assigned instrument.
- Take turns until all have had a chance to play their parts. (The instruments can often be placed so that the others in the group can stand just behind the player to watch and to help.)

2. Teach the instrument parts for the refrain.

Have the students:

- Form four groups (three for the barred instrument parts, one for the guiro part).
- Learn the rhythm of each part with body percussion while singing the song.
- Learn the pitches of the barred instrument parts by echoing while doing the body percussion, or by reading from your hand staff or from notation.
- Sing the refrain as one person from each group plays the part on an assigned instrument.
- Take turns until all have had a chance to play their parts.

3. Combine the two sections.

Have the students:

- Review or learn the recorder part for the refrain.
- Decide who will play each of the instruments. (There should be several recorder players.)
- Sing the entire song with the accompaniment. (See Pupils Edition pages 154 for verse 2.)

FORM

Introduction (measures 1–4):	AG/SX, AX/AM, BX/BM, WB
Verse 1:	Voice, AG/SX, AX/AM, BX/BM, F. Cym., WB
Refrain:	Voice, SM, AM, BX, Rec., Güiro
Verse 2:	Same as verse 1
Refrain:	Same as refrain above

NOTEWORTHY

Rhythm:	$\frac{4}{4}$ meter; whole, half, quarter, and eighth notes; beat; strong beat
Melody:	minor/major comparison
Harmony:	i-iv in minor, I-V in major

0·8 Erie Canal

American Work Song
Arranged by Nancy Ferguson

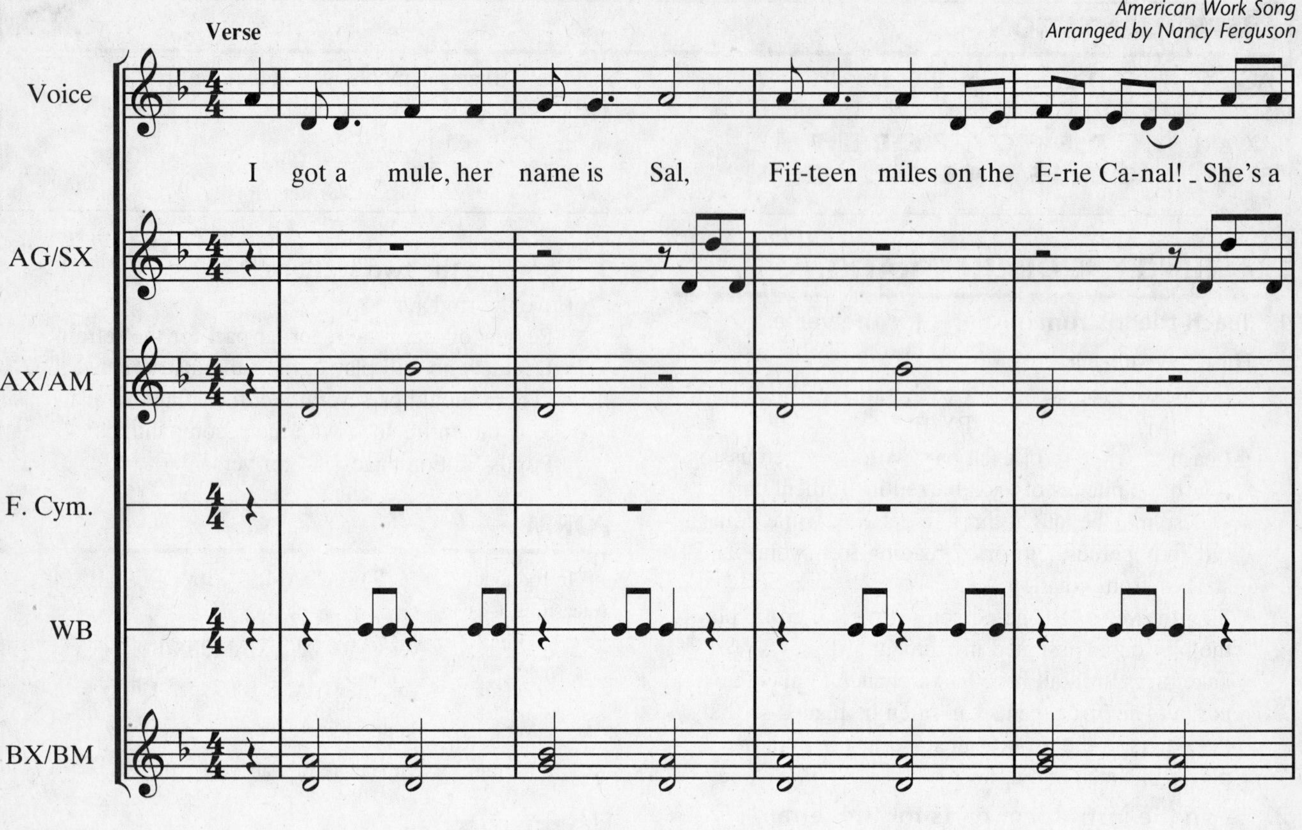

Voice
hauled some barg-es in our day, Filled with lum-ber, coal and hay. And
AG/SX
AX/AM
F. Cym.
WB
BX/BM
Voice
we know ev-'ry inch of the way From Al-ba-ny to Buf-fa-lo.
AG/SX
AX/AM
F. Cym.
WB
BX/BM

Erie Canal (continued)

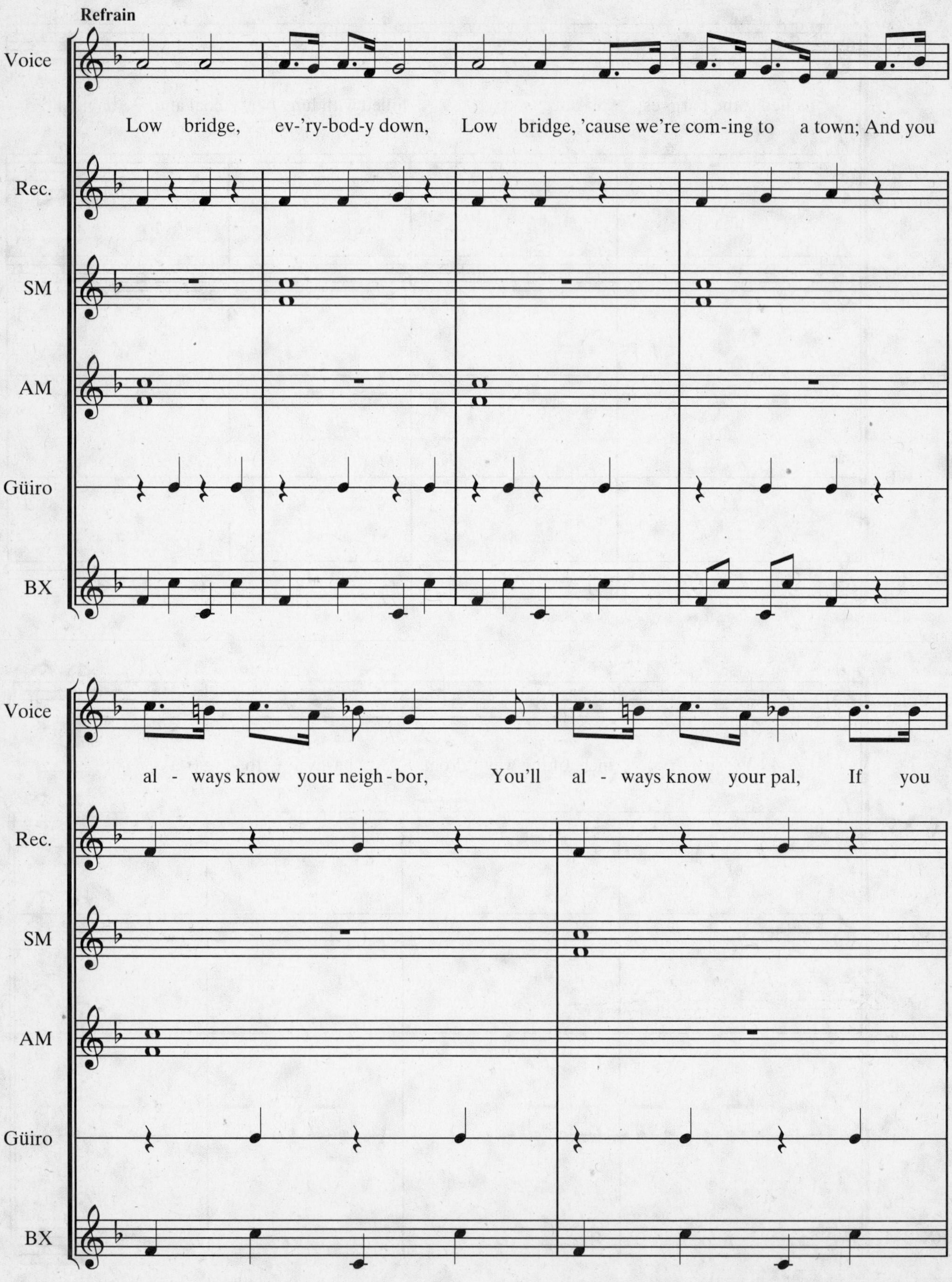

Refrain

Voice

Low bridge, ev-'ry-bod-y down, Low bridge, 'cause we're com-ing to a town; And you

Rec.

SM

AM

Güiro

BX

Voice
ev - er nav - i - gat - ed on the E - rie Ca - nal.
Rec.
SM
AM
Güiro
BX

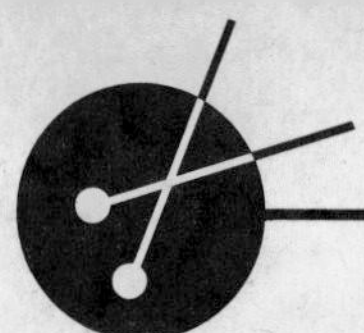

0•9 Down the River

INSTRUMENTATION

AG	□ □ □ □ □ **A B♭ C D E F G A**	tambourine, finger cymbals, hand drum
AX/AM	**C D** □ **F G A B♭ C D** □ □ □ □	
BX/BM	**C** □ □ **F** □ □ **B♭ C** □ □ □ □ □ □	

TEACHING THE ORCHESTRATION

1. **Teach the bass xylophone part in the verse.**

Have the students:
- Pat the rhythm of the BX part with alternating hands as they sing the verse.
- Play the BX part in the air, mirroring you.
- Pat the rhythm of the BX part as they sing the pitch names.
- Take turns playing the BX part on any available barred instruments.
- Sing the verse as one student plays the BX part.

2. **Teach the alto xylophone/alto metallophone part.**

Have the students:
- Play the AX/AM part in the air, mirroring you, as they sing the verse.
- Play in the air, mirroring you, listening as you sing the pitch names of the upper voice. Repeat, singing the pitch names of the upper voice with you.
- Use the same process for the lower voice.
- Look at notation on a chart or chalkboard, and play in the air while singing the verse.
- Take turns playing the AX/AM part on any available barred instruments.
- Sing the verse as some students play the AX/AM and BX parts.

3. **Add the tambourine part.**

Have the students:
- Clap the rhythm of the tambourine part as they sing the verse.
- Practice holding the tambourine upright with one hand and rapidly shaking it for the dotted quarter note roll, then striking the head with the left hand for the following quarter note.
- Combine with the BX part, then all three parts together. Have some students play the parts as all sing the verse.

4. **Teach the bass xylophone and the bass metallophone parts in the refrain.**

Have the students:
- Echo-clap the rhythm of the BX/BM part (three full measures ending on the downbeat of measure four, then three full measures ending on the downbeat of measure eight).
- Perform the rhythm above and listen for the additional notes, to be added by you, in measures four and eight.
- Echo-clap the entire eight measures or read it from notation.
- Play in the air while echo-singing the BX/BM part with pitch letter names.
- Take turns playing the BX/BM part on any available barred instruments.
- Sing the refrain as some students play the BX/BM part.

5. **Add the hand drum part in the refrain.**

Have the students:
- Clap the rhythm of the BX/BM part while you clap the hand drum part.
- Form two groups, one to clap the BX/BM part while the other claps the hand drum part with you. Switch parts.
- Practice holding one hand open as the other hand lightly taps the rhythm on it with three fingers. This is to imitate the motion of striking the hand drum by the rim.
- Take turns playing the hand drum part.
- Combine with the other instrument parts previously learned.

6. **Add the alto glockenspiel part.**

Have the students:

- Identify the pitch letter names for the AG part by looking at notation. (A B♭ C D E F G A)
- Follow the notation as you play it on any instrument, stopping randomly, and tell the letter name of the last pitch you played. (The purpose of this game is to help students internalize the melody as they practice note reading. Return to the beginning after each stop. Do not have the students raise their hands to volunteer. Randomly call on several students at each stopping point.)
- Analyze the patterns in this part, then play it in the air, singing the pitch letter names.
- Take turns playing the AG part on any available barred instruments.
- Sing the refrain as some students play the AG, BX and BM parts.

7. **Culminating performance.**

Have the students:

- Form groups for singing, playing, and movement. Decide on the number of repetitions and perform the entire piece with singing, movement, and instruments. (See Teachers Edition page 167 for movement instructions.)

FORM

Verse:	Voice, AX/AM, BX, Tamb.
Refrain:	Voice, AG, BX/BM, HD

NOTEWORTHY

Rhythm:	$\frac{6}{8}$ meter, dotted quarter notes, eighth notes
Harmony:	I-IV-V

0·9 Down the River

American River Chantey
Arranged by Nancy L. T. Miller

Refrain
Voice
we go sail - ing a - long.
Down the riv - er, Oh,
AG
AX/AM
Tamb./
HD
HD
BX
BM
Voice
down the riv - er, Oh, down the riv - er we go.
AG
AX/AM
Tamb./
HD
BX
BM

Down the River (continued)

Macmillan/McGraw-Hill

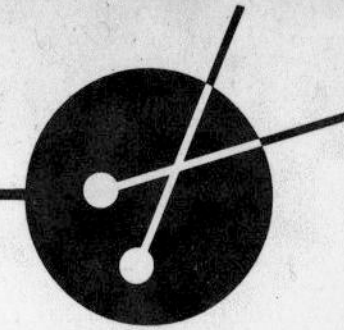

0·10 Et tan' patate là cuite
(Potato's Done)

INSTRUMENTATION

AG	□ □ □ **F** □ □ □ □ □ □ **F** □ □	recorder, bongo drums, tambourine
AX	□ □ **E F G A** □ □ □ □ □ □ □ □	
BX	**C** □ □ **F** □ □ □ **C** □ □ □ □ □ □	

TEACHING THE ORCHESTRATION

1. **Teach the bass xylophone part in the A section.**
   Have the students:
   - Pat the rhythm of the BX part with alternating hands on right thigh (C) and left thigh (F and C) as they sing the A section.
   - Form two groups, one group to sing the A section melody while the other group claps the BX rhythm. Switch parts. Repeat, as one student plays the BX part.
   - Take turns playing the BX part on any available barred instruments.
   - Sing the A section as one student plays the BX part.
2. **Teach the alto xylophone part.**
   Have the students:
   - Clap the rhythm of the AX part as they sing the A section, then as they sing the pitch names of the part.
   - Form two groups, one group to sing the A section melody while the other pats the AX part. Switch parts.
   - Take turns playing the AX part on any available barred instruments.
   - Sing the A section as some students play the AX and BX parts.
3. **Add the bongo part.**
   Have the students:
   - Pat the rhythm of the bongo part using alternating hands, right thigh for higher notes, left thigh for lower notes.
   - Form two groups, one group to sing the A section melody while the other pats the bongo part. Switch parts.
   - Take turns combining the bongo part with the BX part, then combine all three parts together.
   - Sing the A section as some students play the AX, BX, and bongo drum parts.
4. **Teach the bass xylophone part in the B section.**
   Have the students:
   - Learn to pat the rhythm of the BX part as they sing the B section.
   - Play the BX part in the air, mirroring you, singing the pitch letter names.
   - Take turns playing the BX part on any available barred instruments.
   - Sing the B section as one student plays the BX part.
5. **Add the alto glockenspiel and tambourine parts in the B section.**
   Have the students:
   - Snap [L-R] the rhythm of the AG part as they sing the B section.
   - Take turns playing the AG part on any available barred instruments.
   - Sing the song as some students play the AG and BX parts.
   - Mime the tambourine part, mirroring you. (Shake one hand in the air on the quarter note tremolo and tap the palm of that hand with the fingers of the other hand on the tied eighth note. Use a tongue trill for the tremolo sound.)
   - Form two groups, one to sing the B section and one to perform the AG and tambourine parts with body percussion. Divide the second group into two sections, one to snap the AG part, the other to mime the tambourine part, with the tongue trill on the tremolo.
   - Transfer the parts from body percussion to the appropriate instruments. (Practice holding the tambourine upright with one hand and rapidly shaking it for the quarter-note roll, then striking the head with the left hand for the eighth note.)
   - Combine with the BX part previously learned and perform the entire B section.
6. **Culminating performance.**
   Have the students:
   - Perform the entire piece with the instrumental accompaniment. If possible, have recorders play the melody as some students perform the movement. (See Teachers Edition page 164 for information about movement.)

FORM

A: Voice, AX, BX, Bongos, Rec.
B: Voice, AG, BX, Tamb., Rec.
A: Voice, AX, BX, Bongos, Rec.

NOTEWORTHY

Rhythm:	syncopation (sixteenth-eighth-sixteenth), eighth notes, sixteenth notes
Harmony:	I-V
Melody:	F Major

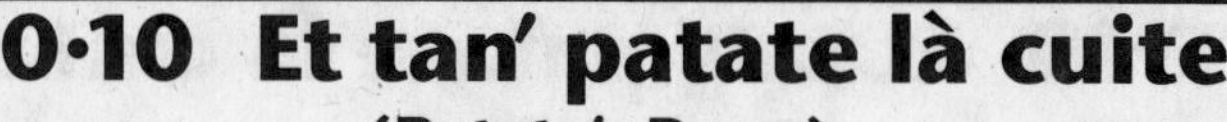

0·10 Et tan′ patate là cuite

(Potato's Done)

Traditional French Creole Song
English Words by MMH
Arranged by Judy Bond

Voice (Rec.)

Po - ta - to's done, it's time to eat it, time to eat it

AX

Bongos

Tamb.

BX

Voice (Rec.)

now. Po - ta - to's done, it's time to eat it,

AX

Bongos

Tamb.

BX

Fine
Voice (Rec.)
time to eat it now!
Whe-ther it's in the pan,
(Change to AG)
AX
Bongos
Tamb.
BX
Voice (Rec.)
Whe-ther it's in the coals,
Whe-ther it's in the
AG
Bongos
Tamb.
BX

Et tan' patate là cuite (continued)

0·11 Pat Works on the Railway

INSTRUMENTATION

AG/SX	□ □ E □ G A □ □ D E □ □ □	finger cymbals, tambourine, snare drums
AX/AM	□ □ E □ G □ B □ D E □ □ □	
BX/BM	□ □ E □ G □ B □ D □ □ □ □	

TEACHING THE ORCHESTRATION

1. Teach the finger cymbals, tambourine, and snare drum parts for the interlude.

Have the students:

- Echo the three parts with body percussion as indicated in the score.
- Take turns playing these patterns on finger cymbals, tambourine, and snare drum—patting the snare drum part, clapping the tambourine part, and snapping the finger cymbals part.
- Sing the song as assigned students play the unpitched instruments during the refrain and interlude.

2. Teach the bass xylophone/bass metallophone part.

Have the students:

- Sing the first verse of the song as they do the following body percussion:

- Take turns playing A and E' in place of the pat and C' and G' in place of the clap as all sing the first verse of the song. (For an easier version, this pattern may be divided between two students on each instrument—one playing the upper notes and the other playing the lower notes.)

3. Teach the alto xylophone/alto metallophone part.

Have the students:

- Play the same body percussion pattern as performed by the bass xylophone and bass metallophone, but with alternating hands (left-right) throughout. (Note the two Es in measure 8.)
- Take turns playing with the first verse of the song, along with the bass instruments.

4. Teach the finger cymbal part.

Have the students:

- Mirror you in clapping the rhythm of the finger cymbal part.
- Sing the first verse as one person plays this part.
- Sing the first verse of the song with all the instrument parts learned so far.

5. Teach the alto glockenspiel/soprano xylophone part.

Have the students:

- Echo-sing the pitches.
- Sing the refrain as two students play the AG/SX part.
- Perform the complete orchestration, the song, and the dance. (See Pupils Edition page 169 for additional verses. See Teachers Edition page 171 for dance instruction.)

FORM

Introduction (measures 1–8):	AX/AM, BX/BM, F. Cym.
Verse 1:	Voice, AX/AM, BX/BM, F. Cym.
Refrain:	*tutti*
Interlude:	AG/SX, AX/AM, BX, BM, F. Cym., Tamb., SD
Verse 2:	Same as verse 1
Refrain:	*tutti*
Verse 3:	Same as verse 1
Refrain:	*tutti*

NOTEWORTHY

Rhythm:	$\frac{6}{8}$ meter
Melody:	E minor
Harmony:	i-III

0·11 Pat Works on the Railway

American Railroad Song
Arranged by Carol King

Macmillan/McGraw-Hill

Pat Works on the Railway (continued)

Voice
AG/SX
AX/AM
F. Cym.
Tamb.
SD
BX/BM

Fil - li - me - oo - re - i - re - ay, To work up - on the rail - way.

Fine

Interlude

Voice
AG/SX
AX/AM
F. Cym.
Tamb.
SD
BX/BM

D.C. al Fine
Voice
AG/SX
AX/AM
F. Cym.
Tamb.
SD
BX/BM

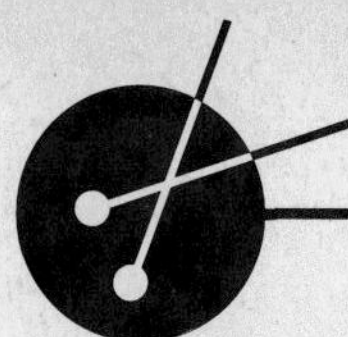

0·12 Simple Gifts

INSTRUMENTATION

AG	□	**D**	□	□	□	□	□	□	**D**	□	□	□	□
SM	□	**D**	□	□	□	□	□	□	**D**	□	□	□	□
AM	□	**D**	□	□	□	□	□	□	□	□	□	□	□
BX/BM	□	**D**	□	□	**G**	□	□	□	□	□	□	□	□
SG	□	□	□	□	**G**	**A**	**B**	**C**	**D**	**E**	**F♯**	**G**	□

finger cymbals, güiro, suspended cymbal, bass bars (all opt.)

TEACHING THE ORCHESTRATION

1. Teach the bass xylophone/bass metallophone part in the A section.

(This part may be doubled by the bass bars if they are available.)

Have the students:

- Pat the rhythm of the BX/BM part as they sing the A section.
- Mirror you as they sing the pitch names and pat the rhythm on each knee, using the right knee for the G, the left knee for the D, and the outside of the right knee for high D.
- Take turns playing the BX/BM part on any available barred instruments.
- Sing the A section as one student plays the BX/BM part.

2. Teach the alto metallophone part in the A section.

Have the students:

- Pat the rhythm of the AM part. Describe how it is different from the BX/BM part. (The AM part is all on the same pitch, while the BX/BM part has three pitches: G, D, and D'. The BX/BM part has one more note than the AM part, the high D which comes before *when.*
- Take turns playing the AM part on any available barred instruments.
- Sing the A section as some students play the AM and BX/BM parts.

3. Add the alto glockenspiel and soprano metallophone parts in the A section.

Have the students:

- Snap the rhythm of the AG and SM parts as they sing the song.
- Take turns playing the AG and SM parts on any available barred instruments.
- Combine the AG and SM parts with the other parts previously learned as they sing the A section.

4. Teach the bass xylophone/bass metallophone and alto metallophone parts in the B section.

Have the students:

- Pat the rhythm of the BX/BM part as they sing the B section.
- Mirror you as they review patting the BX/BM part as in Step 1.
- Analyze this part by comparing it to the BX/BM part in the A section. (The two parts have the same rhythm pattern but the pattern of pitch changes is different because the harmony of the A section is different from the harmony of the B section.)
- Take turns playing the BX/BM part on any available barred instruments.
- Take turns playing the AM part on any available barred instruments. (Notice that this part is the same for both sections.)
- Sing the B section as some students play the BX/BM and AM parts.

5. Add the alto glockenspiel and soprano metallophone parts in the B section.

Have the students:

- Form two groups, one to snap the rhythm of the SM part; the other to clap the rhythm of the AG part. Switch parts.
- Take turns playing the AG and SM parts on any available barred instruments.
- Combine the AG and SM parts with the other parts previously learned as they sing the B section.

6. Teach the finger cymbals, güiro and suspended cymbals parts in the B section.

Have the students:

- Perform the following body percussion:

- Transfer the pats to the suspended cymbal, the claps to the güiro, and the snaps to the finger cymbals.
- Sing the entire song as they perform the parts learned.

7. Add the soprano glockenspiel part in the B section.

Have the students:

- Clap the rhythm of the SG part as they sing the B section, then as they sing the pitch names.
- Take turns playing the SG part on any available barred instruments.
- Gradually combine the SG part with the other parts previously learned.

FORM

A: Voice, AG, SM, AM, BX/BM

B: Voice, SG, AG, SM, AM, BX/BM, S. Cym., Güiro, F. Cym.

NOTEWORTHY

Rhythm: syncopation (sixteenth-eighth-sixteenth), eighth notes

Melody: G Major

Harmony: I-V

0·12 Simple Gifts

Shaker Song
Arranged by Konnie Saliba

Macmillan/McGraw-Hill

Voice
gift to come down where we ought to be. And when we find our-selves in the
SG
AG
SM
AM
F. Cym.
Güiro
S. Cym.
BX/BM/
(B.Bars)

Voice
place just right, 'Twill be in the val - ley of love and de-light. When true sim-
SG
AG
SM
AM
F. Cym.
Güiro
S. Cym.
BX/BM/
(B.Bars)

Voice
pli - ci - ty is gained, To bow and to bend we shan't be a-shamed. To
SG
AG
SM
AM
F. Cym.
Güiro
S. Cym.
BX/BM/
(B.Bars)

Simple Gifts (continued)

Macmillan/McGraw-Hill

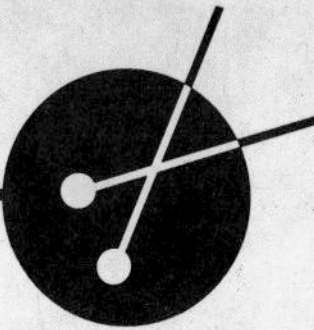

0·13 Ezekiel Saw de Wheel

INSTRUMENTATION

AG	□ □ □ □ □ A □ C D □ □ □ □	conga drum
AX	□ □ □ □ A □ □ C D □ □ □ □	
BX	C □ □ F □ □ □ □ □ □ □ □ □	

TEACHING THE ORCHESTRATION

1. Teach the bass xylophone part.

Have the students:

- Pat the rhythm of the BX part as they sing the song, then as they sing the pitch letter names or pitch syllables of the part.
- Form two groups, one to sing the song while the other sings the BX part with pitch letter names, a neutral syllable, or made-up words. (Those who sing the BX part should also play in the air.)

2. Teach the alto glockenspiel part.

Have the students:

- Echo-sing the AG part with pitch letter names or pitch syllables.
- Play the AG part in the air, singing letter names.
- In three groups, sing the song and the AG and BX parts, while playing in the air.

3. Teach the alto xylophone part.

Have the students:

- Pat the rhythm of the AX part as they sing the song, then as they sing the pitch names of the part.
- In four groups, sing the song and the AX, AG and BX parts.

4. Add the conga drum part.

Have the students:

- Pat the rhythm of the conga drum part as they sing the song.
- Take turns playing the conga drum part with the song.

5. Culminating performance.

Have the students:

- Transfer the BX, AG, and AX parts to the appropriate instruments, reviewing each one.
- Sing the song and play the accompaniment.

FORM

Song: Voice, AG, AX, BX, Conga

NOTEWORTHY

Rhythm: eighth notes, sixteenth notes

Harmony: I-V

0·13 Ezekiel Saw de Wheel

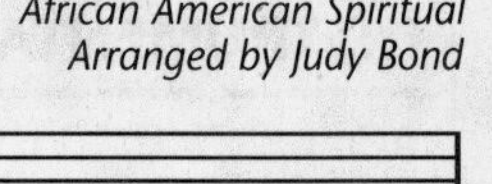
African American Spiritual
Arranged by Judy Bond

Voice
wheel 'way in de mid'l of de air. De big wheel run by
AG
AX
Conga
BX
Voice
faith, An' de lit'l' wheel run by de grace of God. A
AG
AX
Conga
BX

Ezekiel Saw de Wheel (continued)

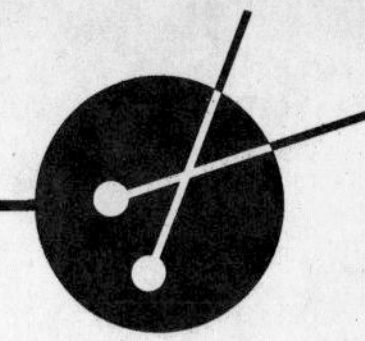

0·14 El quelite
(The Village)

INSTRUMENTATION

SG	□□□□□□□ **C D E F G A**	maracas, claves
AG	□□□□□ **A B♭ C D E F G A**	
AX	□□ **E F G A B♭ C** □□□□□□	
AM	□□□□ **G A B♭** □□□□□□□	
BX	□□ **E F G A B♭ C D** □ **F** □□	

TEACHING THE ORCHESTRATION

1. Teach the bass xylophone part in the A section.

Have the students:
- Pat the rhythm of the BX part as they sing the verse, using the following hand pattern: left-right-left, left-right-left. (You may wish to have the class move first in a gallop-step to prepare this rhythm.)
- Play the BX part in the air, mirroring you. Analyze and describe this part. (There is a two-measure introduction. The A-section melody is eight measures long and is sung twice, ending on A the first time and on F the second time. The BX part is the same both times, except for the last note.)
- Pat the rhythm of the BX part as they sing the pitch names.
- Take turns playing the BX part on any available barred instruments.
- Sing the A section of the melody as one student plays the BX part.

2. Teach the maracas part.

Have the students:
- Form two groups. Have one group pat the rhythm of the BX part as in Step 1, as the other group claps the rhythm of the maracas part. Describe how the parts relate to each other. (The BX plays on all stressed beats. The maracas play mostly after the BX, on unstressed beats.)
- Take turns playing the maracas part with the BX part.

3. Add the claves part.

Have the students:
- Clap the rhythm of the claves part. Describe how it relates to the maracas and the BX part. (The first note of the claves part plays with the first note of the BX part. The second note of the claves part plays with the third note of the maracas part.) This combination of stressed and unstressed beats adds syncopation to the accompaniment.)
- Take turns playing the claves part with the maracas and the BX part.

4. Teach the alto xylophone part.

Have the students:
- Listen and follow notation on a chart or the chalkboard as you point and sing the upper voice of the AX part with pitch letter names or a neutral syllable.
- Sing as you did, playing in the air with the right hand, then follow the same procedure for the lower voice, playing in the air with the left hand.
- In two groups, sing the AX part while playing in the air with both hands. (Students choose to sing the upper or lower voice.)
- Repeat, as one student plays the BX part.
- Take turns playing the AX part on any available barred instruments, with the BX part.
- Sing the A section as some students play the AX, maracas, claves and BX parts.

5. Add the soprano glockenspiel part.

Have the students:
- Play the BX and AX parts while you sing the SG part with pitch letter names. (This part is added when the A section repeats with new words. Sing it in the most comfortable vocal range while playing in the air.)
- Analyze and describe this part. (There are two broken chord patterns, A F C and G E C. Each pattern is played after a descending pattern in the AX. Each pattern starts on an unstressed beat and leads to a stressed beat.)
- Follow you, singing this part and playing it in the air while some students play the AX and BX parts.
- Take turns playing the SG part on any available barred instruments.
- Sing the A section with the entire instrumentation.

6. Teach the bass xylophone part in the B section.

Have the students:
- Mirror you as they pat the rhythm of the BX part across their laps, going from left to right, using alternating hands, beginning with the left hand. At the same time, they sing the B section of the melody.

El quelite (continued)

Note where the harmonic changes occur in the melody. (There are three different chords: I, IV, V.)

- Take turns playing the BX part on any available barred instruments.
- Sing the B section as some students play the BX part.

7. Add the alto metallophone and wind chime parts.

Have the students:

- Mirror you, snapping the rhythm of the AM part as one student plays the BX part.
- Play the part in the air, singing the pitch letter names as you point to notation.
- Transfer the part to AM and play it with the BX part.
- Sing the B section of the melody with all the barred instrument parts, adding wind chimes on the down-beat of every other measure.

8. Add the alto glockenspiel part.

Have the students:

- Analyze and describe the AG part by looking at notation on a chart or the chalkboard. (This part follows the rhythm of the melody, without the upbeats, creating a harmony part parallel with the melody.)
- Echo-sing and echo-play each two-measure segment of this part. (Sing the part an octave below the pitch notated on the score, with pitch letter names. Students echo on barred instruments or vocally.) Extend to four-measure segments, then the entire eight measures.
- Form two groups, one to sing the melody of the B section while the other sings and plays the AG part.
- Sing the B section with all instrumental parts.

9. Perform the entire song with the accompaniment.

Have the students:

- Review all parts, referring to notation when needed.

FORM

A Section:	Voice, SG, AX, BX, Mar., Cls
B Section:	Voice, AG, AM, BX, W. Ch.

NOTEWORTHY

Rhythm:	syncopation, dotted quarter notes, eighth notes
Harmony:	I-IV-V

0·14 El quelite
(The Village)

Mexican Folk Song
English Words by MMH
Arranged by Nancy Miller

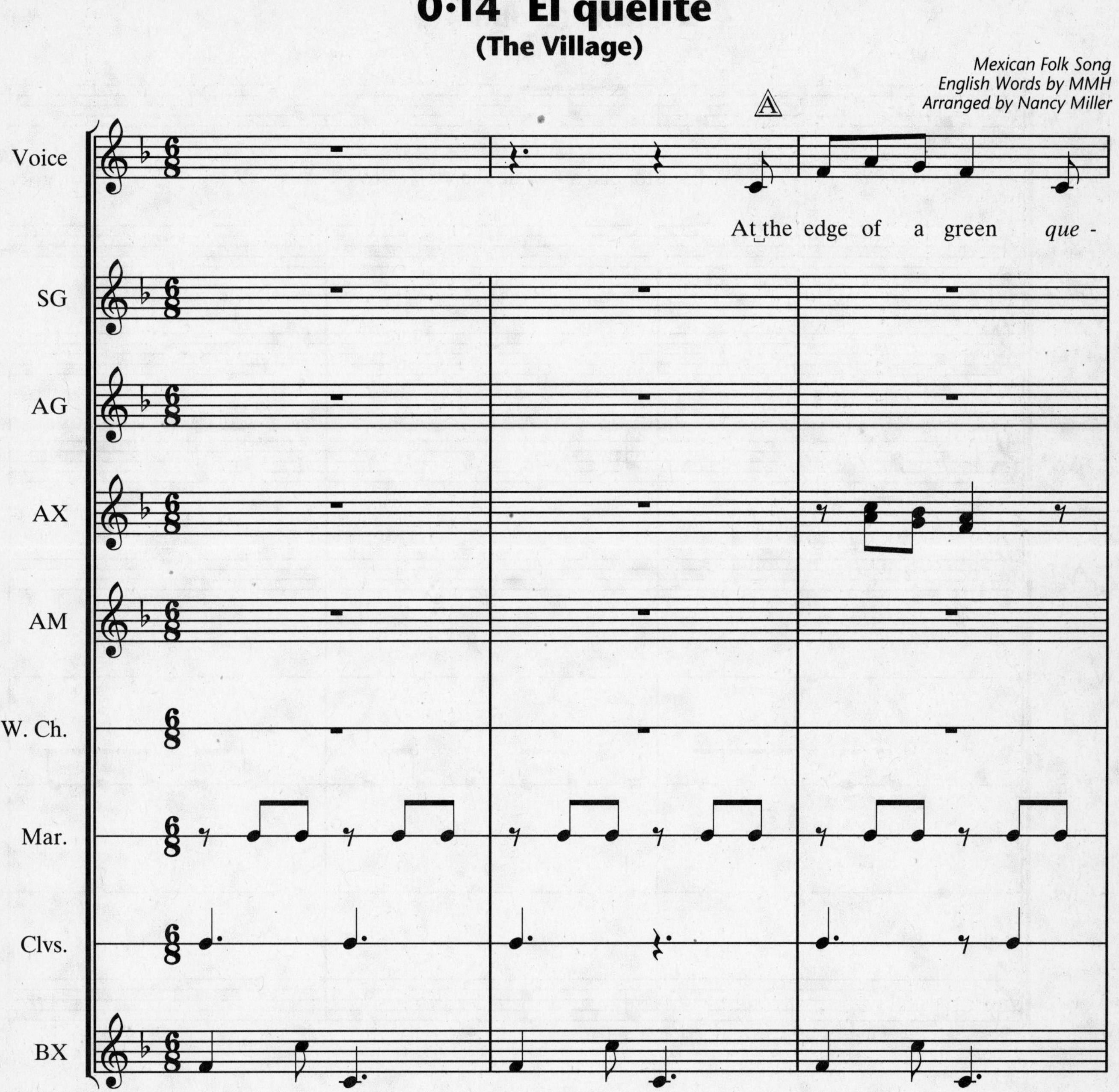

El quelite (continued)

Voice
roos-ter cried out and woke me. He sang a "qui qui ri qui." I
SG
AG
AX
AM
W. Ch.
Mar.
Clvs.
BX

El quelite (continued)

Voice
good. I sing be-cause I feel joy in my
SG
AG
AX
AM
W. Ch.
Mar.
Clvs.
BX

B
Voice
land_ and for - eign lands._
To - mor-row I will be
SG
AG
AX
AM
W. Ch.
Mar.
Clvs.
BX

Macmillan/McGraw-Hill

El quelite (continued)

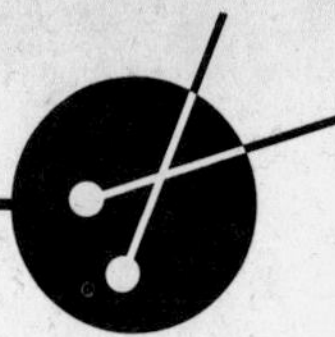

0·15 Joe Turner Blues

INSTRUMENTATION

AX 1	□ □ □ □ **G A B♭** □ □ □ □ □ □ □	suspended cymbal, tambourine
AX 2	**C** □ **E F G** □ □ □ □ □ □ □ □ □	
BX	**C** □ □ **F G** □ □ **C D E** □ □ □	

TEACHING THE ORCHESTRATION

1. Teach the bass xylophone part.

Have the students:

- Pat the rhythm of the BX part as they sing the song, moving the right hand slightly to the right of the thigh on the second and fourth beats.
- Label the first chord of each measure of the BX part, on the board or another visual:

I

IV

V

- Pat the BX part as they call the chord changes.
- Take turns playing the BX part on any available barred instruments.
- Sing the song as some students play the BX part.

2. Add the suspended cymbal part.

Have the students:

- Pat the rhythm of the cymbal part with one hand as they vocalize the rhythm with *ch ch ch ch*:

- Form two groups, one to sing while the other performs the cymbal part as above.
- Take turns playing the cymbal part with the bass xylophone part as they sing the song.

3. Teach the tambourine part.

Have the students:

- Clap the rhythm of the tambourine part as they sing the song. Analyze and describe the tambourine part. (The tambourine plays on beats 2 and 4, the unstressed beats.)
- Take turns playing the tambourine with the bass xylophone and cymbal part as they sing the song.

4. Add the alto xylophone 1 and alto xylophone 2 parts.

Have the students:

- Sing the song and play the BX, cymbal, and tambourine parts while the teacher adds the AX 1 part. (This may be sung with scat syllables or with words such as "Yes he's gone, Joe Turner's gone", or played on recorder or any pitched instrument. For best results, first demonstrate this part vocally, then with an instrument.)
- Take turns singing or playing the AX 1 part while other students sing and play the other parts.
- Analyze the AX 2 part by looking at notation and comparing it with AX 1. (AX 2 starts a third lower. It follows the same basic pattern, but has an additional pitch.)
- Learn the AX 2 part in the same way AX 1 was learned.
- With a partner, sing or play AX 1 and AX 2 together while other students perform the other parts.

5. Culminating performance.

Have the students:

- Experiment with different combinations of instruments and singing for the AX 1 and AX 2 parts, using mallet instruments, recorders, and any other available instruments.
- Decide what combinations to use in the final performance.
- Perform the song with all instrumental and vocal parts.

FORM

Verse: Voice, AX 1, AX 2, BX, Tamb., S. Cym.

NOTEWORTHY

Rhythm: syncopation, quarter notes, eighth notes
Melody: C Major
Harmony: I-IV-V

0·15 Joe Turner Blues

American Blues
Arranged by Doug Goodkin

Voice
Turn-er's come and gone. He
AX 1
AX 2
S. Cym.
Tamb.
BX
Voice
left me here to sing this song.
AX 1
AX 2
S. Cym.
Tamb.
BX

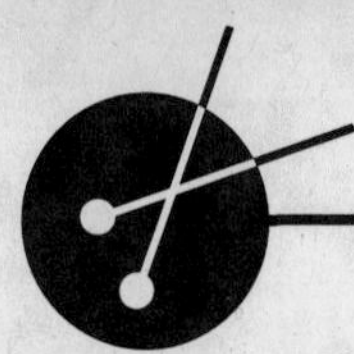

0·16 Nottamun Town

INSTRUMENTATION

SG/AG ☐ D ☐ F G A ☐ C D ☐ F G A — finger cymbals
BM ☐ D ☐ ☐ ☐ ☐ ☐ ☐ ☐ ☐ ☐ ☐ ☐ ☐ ☐

TEACHING THE ORCHESTRATION

1. **Teach the bass metallophone part.**

   Have the students:
   - Mirror you as you show a tremolo with your hands on one knee. (You may choose to have the students play the tremolo D in another way: holding two mallets in one hand, handles touching together in the palm making a "V" shape, one mallet over the end of the metallophone bar and one mallet under the bar, moving the hand quickly up and down.)
   - Sing the song as one student plays the BM part.

2. **Add the finger cymbals part.**

   Have the students:
   - Play imaginary finger cymbals in the air on the first and last beats as they sing the song.
   - Sing the song with BM and finger cymbals.

3. **Add the soprano glockenspiel/alto glockenspiel part.**

   Have the students:
   - Mirror you, playing the SG/AG part in the air as they sing the song.
   - Sing the song and take turns playing the SG/AG part on any available barred instruments, randomly choosing any two of the following pitches: D F G A C' D' F' G' A'. (Effective chord clusters will result if there are at least three barred instruments. SM and AM may be added to this part.)
   - Sing the song as some students play the SG/AG and BM parts.

4. **Perform the song with accompaniment.**

   Have the students:
   - Sing the song and play all instrumental parts.

FORM

Verse: Voice, SG/SM, BM, F. Cym.

NOTEWORTHY

Rhythm: $\frac{3}{2}$ - $\frac{2}{2}$ changing meter, triplets
Melody: pentatonic
Harmony: tonic pedal

0·16 Nottamun Town

English Folk Song
Arranged by Marilyn Davidson

Voice
SG/AG
F. Cym.
BM

In Not - ta - mun town, not a soul would look

up. Not a soul would look up, not a soul would look

(any two pitches)

Voice
down. Not a soul would look up, not a soul would look
SG/AG
F. Cym.
BM

Voice
down to show me the way to fair Not-ta-mun town.
SG/AG
F. Cym.
BM

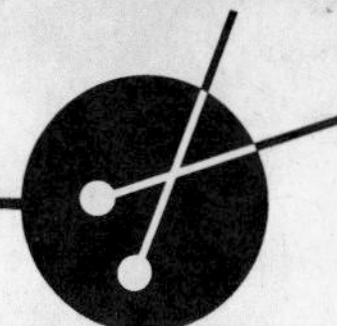

0·17 The Horseman

INSTRUMENTATION

SG/AG	☐ D ☐ ☐ ☐ ☐ ☐ ☐ D ☐ ☐ ☐ ☐	recorder (opt.), temple blocks, timpani (tuned to D)
SM	☐ D ☐ ☐ ☐ A ☐ ☐ ☐ ☐ ☐ ☐ ☐	
AX	☐ D ☐ ☐ ☐ ☐ ☐ ☐ ☐ ☐ ☐ ☐ ☐	
AM	☐ D ☐ ☐ ☐ A ☐ ☐ ☐ ☐ ☐ ☐ ☐	
BX/BM	☐ D ☐ ☐ ☐ ☐ ☐ ☐ ☐ ☐ ☐ ☐ ☐	

TEACHING THE ORCHESTRATION

1. Prepare to teach the rhythms of all of the instrument patterns.

Have the students:

- Form five groups. Each group is to practice the rhythm of a different part as they say chants drawn from the poem "The Headless Horseman Rides Tonight." (See Pupils Edition page 294.) Assign two or three students to each instrument part, depending upon the size of the class.

2. Teach the alto xylophone part.

Have the students:

- Echo and then pat the rhythm of the AX part as they mirror you, saying *Galloping on! Galloping on! Galloping on! On! On! On!*
- Sing the song as the AX group pats the rhythm of its part.

Note: Because all of the patterns begin on the downbeat of the first *full* measure of the voice part, the instruments should always play from the beginning of the four-measure pattern, with the voice part beginning after the first beat.

3. Teach the bass xylophone/bass metallophone and timpani parts.

Have the students:

- Echo and then pat the rhythm of the BX/BM and timpani parts as they mirror you, as they say *Wind! Wind! Wind! He rides upon the...*
- Sing the song as this group pats the rhythm of the parts.
- Sing the song as both groups do their assigned body-percussion patterns, practicing until they can maintain the patterns without your help.

4. Teach the pattern for the soprano and alto metallophone parts.

Have the students:

- Sing the song as this group pats the rhythm of the AM part and snaps the rhythm of the SM part, first echoing and then mirroring you as they say *Wind! Wind!*
- Sing the song as these three groups do their assigned body-percussion patterns; again, practicing until they can maintain their part without your help.

5. Teach the pattern for the soprano glockenspiel/alto glockenspiel part.

Have the students:

- Sing the song as the SG/AG group snaps the rhythm of its assigned part, first echoing and then mirroring you saying *On! On!* Be sure they understand how this part relates to the endings of each of the four phrases.
- Sing the song as all four groups do their assigned body-percussion patterns.

6. Teach the pattern for the temple blocks part.

Have the students:

- Sing the song as the temple blocks group pats its pattern with alternating hands, mirroring you, saying *Rides upon the wind tonight! He...*

7. Teach the entire orchestration.

Have the students:

- Watch as you show each barred instrument group the pitches to play.
- Take turns playing the instrument(s) assigned to their group with the song.

8. Add an introduction and coda.

Have the students:

- Mirror you to learn the clap/pat pattern shown in the score.
- Practice doing this pattern with a *crescendo* for four measures and a *decrescendo* for four measures. Have them use this as the first part of the introduction, to suggest the horseman riding by. (The pattern is not continued during the song.)
- Learn the second part of the introduction, during which the other instruments begin playing, four measures apart, in this order: temple blocks, timpani, bass xylophone and bass metallophone, alto xylophone, soprano and alto metallophones, soprano and alto glockenspiels.
- Learn to play the coda. (During the coda, the instruments stop playing in the reverse of the order in which they began. As the temple blocks stop, the body percussion should be done as in the introduction, to suggest that the horseman is again passing by.)

9. Add an improvised interlude (to be done between unison and canon versions of the song).

Have the students:

- Sing the song with the accompaniment. Then think through the song as the accompaniment continues, and as students in the SG/AG and AX groups improvise for the length of the song.
- Repeat the entire song, this time having only one of the players in the SG/AG and AX groups improvise. (As an alternative, you may wish to have recorders improvise on C F G A C' D'.)
- Take turns playing the parts until all have had a turn on their assigned parts. (Another day, have the students switch parts.)
- Perform the song, with instruments, as follows: introduction, song in unison, improvisation, song in canon, coda.

FORM

Introduction:	Eight-measure body-percussion pattern, other parts beginning one at a time, four measures apart: TB, Timp., BX/BM, AX, SM/AM, SG/AG
Song:	Voice in unison, *tutti* instruments except body percussion
Interlude:	Improvise SG, AG, AX, or Rec.
Song:	Voice in two-, three-, or four-part canon; *tutti* instruments except body percussion
Coda:	Parts stopping four measures apart: SG/AG, SM/AM, AX, BX/BM, Timp., TB, body-percussion pattern

NOTEWORTHY

Rhythm:	$\frac{6}{8}$
Melody:	D minor
Harmony:	bordun

0·17 The Horseman

Music by Marilyn Davidson
Words by Walter de la Mare
Arranged by Marilyn Davidson

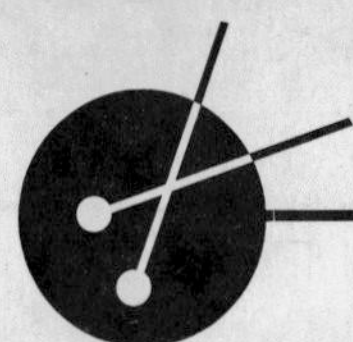

0·18 Nine Hundred Miles

INSTRUMENTATION

AG	☐ ☐ ☐ ☐ ☐ **A** ☐ ☐ ☐ ☐ ☐ ☐ **G A**	wind chimes
AM	☐ ☐ ☐ **F** ☐ **A** ☐ ☐ ☐ ☐ ☐ ☐ ☐ ☐	
BX	☐ **D** ☐ **F** ☐ **A B♭ C D E** ☐ **G** ☐	
BM	☐ **D** ☐ ☐ ☐ **A B♭ C D** ☐ ☐ ☐ ☐	

TEACHING THE ORCHESTRATION

1. **Teach the bass metallophone part.**

Have the students:

- Mirror you, playing measures 1–4 and 13–16 of the BM part in the air while singing the song. (These two 4-measure phrases are identical.)
- Learn the pitch letter names, then take turns playing this part on any available barred instruments while singing the song.
- Sing pitch letter names for the upper voice of the BM part in measures 9–12, as you point to notation on a chart or chalkboard. Repeat for the lower voice.
- Play measures 9–12 in the air, singing first the upper voice, then the lower voice.
- Transfer this part to any available barred instrument and play it with measures 9–12 of the song, then sing the entire song, playing the BM part on measures 1–4, 9–12, and 13–16.
- Mirror you, playing the BM part for measures 5–8 in the air while singing the letter names.
- Add this section to what is already known by singing the entire song with the BM part, still playing it on any available barred instruments, using the written notation as a guide for measures 9–12.
- Sing the song as one student plays the BM part.

2. **Teach the alto glockenspiel part.**

Have the students:

- Snap the rhythm of the SG/AG part as they sing the song.
- Take turns playing the AG part on any available barred instruments.
- Combine the AG part with the BM part.

3. **Add the alto metallophone part.**

Have the students:

- Mirror you, playing the AM part in the air and singing the pitches on *loo* while some students play the BM and AG parts and other students sing the song.
- Transfer this part to AM and play it while continuing to sing the pitches on *loo*, combining it with the song and the BM and AG parts.

4. **Add the bass xylophone part.**

Have the students:

- Echo-sing the pitch letter names of the BX part, reading from notation on a chart or chalkboard. (Use the same sequence as in Step 1, learning measures 1–4 and 13–16, then 9–12, then 5–8.)
- Take turns playing the BX part on any available barred instruments, using the written notation as a guide.
- Sing the song as some students play the BX and BM parts.

5. **Add the wind chimes part and perform the entire song with accompaniment.**

Have the students:

- Review the parts and then sing the song three times, the first time with BX and BM, the second time adding AM and AG, and the third time adding wind chimes. (The student playing the wind chimes should follow your signal. This part can be added without any teaching.)

FORM

Verse: Voice, AG, AM, BX, BM, W. Ch.
Refrain: Voice, AG, AH, BX, BM

NOTEWORTHY

Rhythm: dotted half notes, quarter notes, whole notes
Melody: pentatonic

0·18 Nine Hundred Miles

American Traditional Song
Arranged by Nancy L.T. Miller

Nine Hundred Miles (continued)

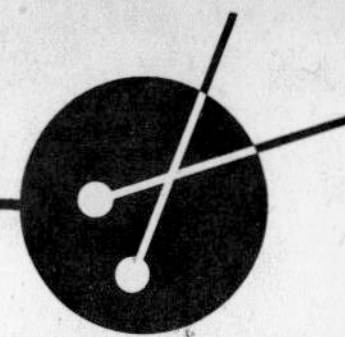

0•19 Going to Boston

INSTRUMENTATION

AX □ □ E F G A B♭ C D □ □ □ □
BX C □ E F G A B♭ C D □ □ □ □

TEACHING THE ORCHESTRATION

1. **Teach the bass xylophone part in the verse.**

   Have the students:
   - Echo-sing the BX part, using the syllable *bom*. (Divide the part into two 4-measure sections. Use hand-levels to indicate pitches.) Sing the entire eight measures and play them in the air.
   - Form three groups. One group sings the BX part, another group plays it on any available barred instruments, and the third group sings the verse. Switch parts.
   - Sing the verse as one student plays the BX part.

2. **Add the alto xylophone part in the verse.**

   Have the students:
   - Form two groups. Have one group pat the rhythm of the BX part as the other group claps the rhythm of the AX part. (You may wish to have them read the parts from the board or another visual.) Decide how the two parts relate. (The BX part plays mostly on the downbeats and the AX parts play on the off-beats.) Switch roles and repeat.
   - Write out the pitch letter names of the chords as shown below:

C'	C'	B♭	C'
G	A	G	G
E	F	F	E
I	IV	V7	I

   - Sing each line of the AX part as some students play the BX part on any barred instrument.
   - Take turns playing the AX part on any available instruments.

Note: Have each student play all three notes of the chords in the AX part by using three mallets, or distribute the notes among two or three players.

   - Sing the verse as some students play the AX and BX parts.

3. **Teach the bass xylophone part in the refrain.**

   Have the students:
   - Mirror you as they play the rhythm of the BX part in the air using both hands while singing the refrain.
   - Take turns playing the BX part on any available barred instruments.
   - Sing the refrain as one student plays the BX part.

4. **Add the alto xylophone part in the refrain.**

   Have the students:
   - Clap the rhythm of the AX part as some students play the BX part. Describe this part. (Rhythmically it is like the AX part in the A section.)
   - Study the letter names of the pitches on a chart or chalkboard as shown below:

C'	C'			C'		C'	C'
G	G	D'	D'	G	G	D'	G
E	E	G	G	E	E	G	E

   - Take turns playing the AX and BX parts on any available instruments.
   - Sing the refrain as some students play the AX and BX parts.

5. **Perform the entire song with accompaniment.**

   Have the students:
   - Sing and play the entire song, using the form listed below as a guide.

FORM

Verse: Voice, AX, BX
Refrain: Voice, AX, BX

NOTEWORTHY

Rhythm: quarter notes, eighth notes
Melody: C Mixolydian
Harmony: Verse: I-IV-V
Refrain: I-V

1·19 Going to Boston

American Sea Chantey
Arranged by Mary Lou Thiel

Voice
AX
BX
Won't we look pret-ty in the ball - room? Won't we look pret-ty in the
ball - room? Ear - ly in the morn - ing.